This book is a record of our baby

....

BABY RECORD BOOK

FLAME TREE
PUBLISHING

Introduction

This book is for you to record and celebrate your baby's first year in the world. With plenty of space to fill in information about your baby's milestones, favourite activities and family, you will create a lasting memory of these precious times. Full of traditional songs and nursery rhymes, there is also space to include your favourite photos, drawings and other special keepsakes, so that you may hand down a lovely record that will be treasured forever.

Contents

3

BIRTH

Waiting for Baby

Date of first ultrasound

....

First felt baby kick

....

First listened to baby's
heartbeat

....

PLACE YOUR PHOTO HERE

Baby's prenatal scan

Day   Date

....

Time   Place

....

The doctor's name was

....

The midwife's name was

....

Visitors

....

....

....

....

5

When Baby was Born

PLACE YOUR PHOTO HERE

I weighed

....

I was .... long

The colour of my eyes were

....

The colour of my hair was

....

Monday's child is fair of face

Tuesday's child is full of grace

Wednesday's child is full of woe

Thursday's child has far to go

Friday's child is loving and giving

Saturday's child works hard for his living

But the child that is born on the Sabbath day

Is bonny and blithe and good and gay.

Special memories

....
....
....
....
....
....
....
....
....
....
....
....

First Greeting Card

Baby's Name

Baby's full name

....

....

My name means

....

....

My name was chosen by

....

....

PLACE YOUR PHOTO HERE

Why we chose your name

....
....
....
....

Other names we thought of

....
....
....
....

Nicknames we called you before you were born

....
....
....
....

PLACE YOUR PHOTO HERE

PLACE YOUR PHOTO HERE

I have no name
I am but two days old —
What shall I call thee?
I happy am
Joy is my name —
Sweet joy befall thee!

Extract from Infant Joy
by William Blake (1757–1827)

Coming Home

Day

Date

Time

Baby was brought home by

....

....

....

....

....

....

....

We lived at

....

....

....

....

....

....

....

....

PLACE YOUR PHOTO HERE

Baby's first home

PLACE YOUR PHOTO HERE

11

FAMILY

My Family Tree

Grandfather .... Grandmother ....   Grandfather .... Grandmother ....

Uncles
....
....
....

Aunts
....
....
....

Uncles
....
....
....

Aunts
....
....
....

Father .... Mother

Brothers
....
....
....

Sisters
....
....
....

Baby
....

13

Baby's Parents

My Mum

Mum's name

....

Maiden name

....

Age

....

Birthday

....

Place of birth

....

Occupation

....

Mum has .... hair

Mum has .... eyes

PLACE YOUR PHOTO HERE

My Dad

Dad's name

....

Age

....

Birthday

....

Place of birth

....

Occupation

....

Dad has .... hair

Dad has .... eyes

He is .... tall

Baby's Brothers and Sisters

My Brothers

Name	Age	Birthday	Eye colour	Hair colour

My Sisters

Name	Age	Birthday	Eye colour	Hair colour

JACK AND JILL

Jack and Jill went up the hill,

to fetch a pail of water;

Jack fell down,

and broke his crown, and

Jill came tumbling after.

Then up Jack got and

off did trot, as fast

as he could caper;

And went to bed and covered his head

In vinegar and brown paper.

PLACE YOUR PHOTO HERE

Baby's First Week

My first visitors

....
....
....
....
....
....
....
....
....

PLACE YOUR PHOTO HERE

PLACE YOUR PHOTO HERE

Special memories

....
....
....
....
....
....
....
....
....
....
....
....
....
....
....
....
....

Special memories

....
....
....
....
....
....
....
....
....
....
....
....
....
....
....
....
....
....

PLACE YOUR PHOTO HERE

BABY'S FAVOURITES

Baby's Favourite Games

Games I like to play	I play them with
Peek-a-boo	
Blocks	

Baby's Favourite Toys

Toys I like to play with	Age
Teddy bear	
Rattle	

19

Baby's Favourite Songs

Songs I like

Twinkle, twinkle little star

Old McDonald had a farm

How I react

PAT-A-CAKE

Pat-a-cake, pat-a-cake,

Baker's man!

Bake me a cake,

As fast as you can.

Pat it, and prick it,

And mark it with B,

Put it in the oven

For Baby and me.

PLACE YOUR PHOTO HERE

Nursery rhymes
I like to hear   Age

Humpty Dumpty ....

Little Miss Muffet ....

....

....

....

....

....

....

....

LITTLE MISS MUFFET

Little Miss Muffet

Sat on a tuffet,

Eating of curds and whey;

There came a big spider,

And sat down beside her,

And frightened

Miss Muffet away.

BABY'S
MILESTONES

Baby's Naming Ceremony

Day

Date

Time

Place

Guests that came

PLACE YOUR PHOTO HERE

PLACE YOUR PHOTO HERE

My Godparents

Baby's Special Occasions

Use these pages to record religious festivals or celebrations in your baby's first year

....
....
....
....
....
....
....
....
....
....
....

PLACE YOUR PHOTO HERE

....
....
....
....
....
....
....
....
....
....
....
....
....
....
....

PLACE YOUR PHOTO HERE

PLACE YOUR PHOTO HERE

What Baby Could Do

PLACE YOUR PHOTO HERE

ACTIVITY	DATE	AGE
I sat up		
I lifted my head		
I rolled over		
I pulled myself up		
I smiled		
I crawled on my tummy		
I crawled on my knees		

PLACE YOUR PHOTO HERE

PLACE YOUR PHOTO HERE

Baby's Bathtime

My first bath at home

....

....

....

....

My first time in the big bath

....

....

....

....

PLACE YOUR PHOTO HERE

PLACE YOUR PHOTO HERE

Games I like to play in the bath

....
....
....
....
....
....
....
....
....
....
....

RUB-A-DUB-DUB

Rub-a-dub-dub
Three men in a tub.

The butcher, the baker
And the candlestick maker.

My favourite bath toy

....
....
....
....

My favourite bathtime game

....
....
....
....
....
....
....
....
....

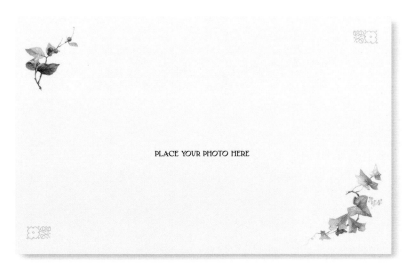

PLACE YOUR PHOTO HERE

Baby in the bath

29

Baby's Bedtime

I first slept in my cot

....

....

....

I first slept through the night

....

....

....

PLACE YOUR PHOTO HERE

The best ways to get me to sleep

....

....

....

....

....

....

....

....

....

My bedtime toys

....
....
....
....
....
....
....
....
....
....
....
....

PLACE YOUR PHOTO HERE

My bedtime is

....
....

Hush-a-Bye, Baby

Hush-a-bye, baby,
on the tree-top!

When the wind blows
the cradle will rock;

When the bough breaks
the cradle will fall;

Down will come baby,
cradle and all.

Baby's Health

My immunisations

IMMUNISATION	DATE	AGE	DOCTOR OR NURSE'S NAME

PLACE YOUR PHOTO HERE

Love me — I love you,
Love me, my baby;
Sing it high, sing it low,
Sing it as may be.

Mother's arms under you;
Her eyes above you;
Sing it high, sing it low,
Love me — I love you.

Love me — I love you
by Christina Rossetti (1830–94)

	THINGS THAT COMFORTED ME
When I was poorly	
When I was teething	

Baby's Growth

PLACE YOUR PHOTO HERE

When the voices of children

are heard on the green

And laughing is heard on the hill,

My heart is at rest within my breast

And everything else is still.

Extract from Nurse's Song

by William Blake (1757—1827)

PLACE YOUR PHOTO HERE

Use this chart to record how much your baby grows over their first 12 months

AGE	WEIGHT	LENGTH
At 1 month		
At 2 months		
At 3 months		
At 4 months		
At 5 months		
At 6 months		
At 7 months		
At 8 months		
At 9 months		
At 10 months		
At 11 months		
At 12 months		

My first tooth came through on

....

I had all my teeth by

....

I was .... old

Baby's Outings

The Park

....

....

....

....

The Zoo

....

....

....

....

PLACE YOUR PHOTO HERE

PLACE YOUR PHOTO HERE

On a Train

....
....
....
....

On a Teddybear's Picnic

....
....
....
....

Swimming

....
....
....
....

Playschool

....
....
....
....

On the Bus

....
....
....
....

PLACE YOUR PHOTO HERE

Baby's First Christmas

I spent my first Christmas at

....

....

with

....

....

....

I was .... old

PLACE YOUR PHOTO HERE

LITTLE JACK HORNER

Little Jack Horner
Sat in the corner,
Eating of Christmas pie:

He put in his thumb
And pulled out a plum,

And said,
'What a good boy am I!'

Presents

....
....
....
....
....
....
....
....
....
....
....
....
....
....
....
....

PLACE YOUR PHOTO HERE

Baby on Christmas Day

Baby's First Holiday

I went with

....

....

....

We went to

....

....

I was .... old

PLACE YOUR PHOTO HERE

We travelled there by

....

....

....

Date

....

We stayed at

....

....

....

....

....

40

PLACE YOUR PHOTO HERE

Special memories

....
....
....
....
....
....
....
....
....
....
....

Our favourite activities

....
....
....
....
....
....
....
....
....
....
....

PLACE YOUR PHOTO HERE

Baby on Holiday

Baby's First Words

I started to understand words

....
....
....
....

The first time I said mummy

....
....
....
....

I started to copy noises

....
....
....
....

The first time I said daddy

....
....
....
....

WORD	DATE	WHO HEARD IT

Use this chart to record your baby's first words

PLACE YOUR PHOTO HERE

PLACE YOUR PHOTO HERE

Baby's First Birthday

Day
....

Date
....

Time
....

Place
....

How we celebrated
....
....
....
....
....
....
....
....
....
....
....
....
....
....
....
....
....
....
....
....
....
....
....
....
....
....
....

PLACE YOUR PHOTO HERE

PLACE YOUR PHOTO HERE

Special memories

....
....
....
....
....
....
....

Présents

....
....
....
....
....
....

I wore

....
....

Guests

....
....
....
....
....
....
....
....

Our Baby's Future

Record any hopes and dreams
that you have for your
baby's future

....

....

....

....

....

....

....

....

....

THE GRAND OLD DUKE OF YORK

The Grand Old Duke of York he had
ten thousand men
He marched them up to the top of the hill
And he marched them down again.
When they were up, they were up
And when they were down, they were down
And when they were only halfway up
They were neither up nor down.

PLACE YOUR PHOTO HERE

Use this space to show your favourite photo of you and your baby

Publisher and Creative Director: Nick Wells
Project Editor: Chelsea Edwards
Picture Research: Gemma Walters
Art Director: Mike Spender
Digital Design and Production: Chris Herbert
Layout Design: Theresa Maynard

08 10 12 11 09

1 3 5 7 9 10 8 6 4 2

This edition first published 2008 by
FLAME TREE PUBLISHING
Crabtree Hall, Crabtree Lane
Fulham, London SW6 6TY
United Kingdom

www.flametreepublishing.com

Flame Tree Publishing is part of the Foundry Creative Media Co. Ltd.

© 2008 The Foundry Creative Media Co. Ltd.

ISBN 978-1-84786-222-8

Printed in China

Picture Credits

Page 2 and 30: *Mother's Pride* by Leon-Emile Caille (1836–1907), courtesy of The Bridgeman Art Library
Page 4: *The New Arrival* by August Toulmouche (1829–90), © Christie's Images Ltd
Page 6: *Mother and Baby* by Fritz Paulsen (1838–98), courtesy of The Bridgeman Art Library
Page 8: *First Born*, 1863 by Gustave Leonard de Jonghe (1829–93), courtesy of The Bridgeman Art Library
Page 10: *At the Cottage Door* by Helen Allingham (1848–1926), © Christie's Images Ltd
Page 11: *The Priest's House, West Hoathly* by Helen Allingham (1848–1926), © Christie's Images Ltd
Page 12, 13 and 48: *Bubbles: Cottage Scene with Children at Play* by John Dawson Watson (1832–92), courtesy of The Bridgeman Art Library
Page 14: *Hush!* by George Goodwin Kilburne (1839–1924), courtesy of The Bridgeman Art Library
Page 16: *A Rest in the Row* by Rose Maynard Barton (1856–1929), © Christie's Images Ltd
Page 18: *Julia Payne and Her Son Ivan* by Julius Gari Melchers (1860–1932), © Christie's Images Ltd
Page 19: *Watching the Kittens* by Adolphe Weisz (1838–c.1900), © Christie's Images Ltd
Page 2 and 21: *Mother and Child with a Poppy* by Frederick Richard Pickersgill (1820–1900), courtesy of The Bridgeman Art Library
Page 22: *The Return from the Christening* by Hubert Salentin (1822–1910), courtesy of The Bridgeman Art Library
Page 25: *The Master of the House* by George Goodwin Kilburne (1839–1924), © Christie's Images Ltd
Page 26: *The First Step* by Pierre Auguste Renoir (1841–1919), © Christie's Images Ltd
Page 27: *Gabrielle and Jean* by Pierre Auguste Renoir (1841–1919), courtesy of The Bridgeman Art Library
Page 28: *An Earthly Paradise* by Sir Lawrence Alma-Tadema (1836–1912), courtesy of The Bridgeman Art Library
Page 31: *Young Mother from Arles* by Henri Bouchet-Doumeng (19th century), courtesy of The Bridgeman Art Library
Page 33: *Mother and Baby* by Dutch School (19th century), courtesy of The Bridgeman Art Library
Page 36: *Bathers, c. 1913* by Edward Henry Potthast (1857–1927), courtesy of The Bridgeman Art Library
Page 38: *Christmas Eve – A Dream*, courtesy of Foundry Arts/The Laurel Clark Collection
Page 39: *The New Picture Book*, courtesy of Foundry Arts/The Laurel Clark Collection
Page 40: *Her Pride and Joy* by Leon-Emile Caille (1836–1907), © Christie's Images Ltd
Page 42: *Playing with Baby* by Adolf-Julius Berg (1820–76), courtesy of The Bridgeman Art Library
Page 45: *An Interior with a Mother and Child* by George Goodwin Kilburne (1839–1924), © Christie's Images Ltd
Page 46 and 47: *Teatime* by Myles Birket Foster (1825–99), © Christie's Images Ltd